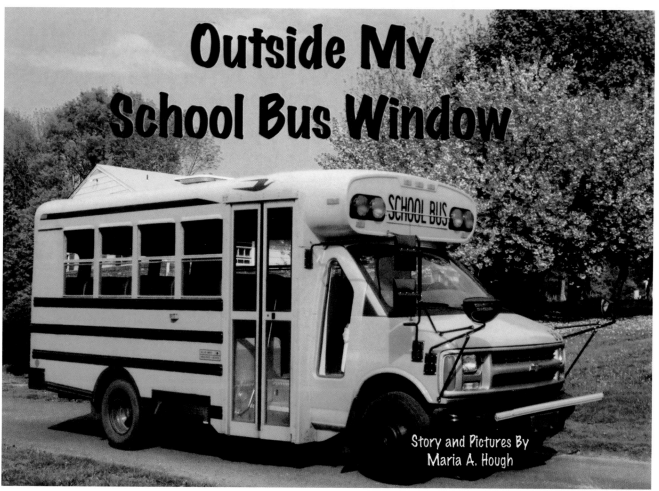

Outside My School Bus Window

Story and Pictures By
Maria A. Hough

Wishing Well Press
1407 Schwenkmill Road
Perkasie, PA 18944
Telephone: (215) 258-1197
Email: wishingwellpress@netzero.net
www.wishingwellpress.com

Publishing services through Mary Lou Gola, Today's Tuesday, Inc.
Cover and text designed by Paul Evans.
Printing by Alcom

First Printing 2006
Printed in the United States of America

ISBN 0-9779248-0-7

Dedication

This book is dedicated to family, friends, co-workers and neighbors
who thought it was a good idea.

A special thanks to present and former Pennridge School District staff:
M. Goldberg, M. Nichols, K. Reed and S. Renshaw
from the first draft your enthusiasm has been inspirational.

This book is based on my actual bus run in the beautiful countryside of Bucks County, Pennsylvania.
It started with the perfect setting, a special group of students and a recurring question - "Did you see...?"
We would take turns filling in the blank. The end result is what you are reading now.

Riding the school bus is a chance to enlighten students about their environment.
Education builds appreciation.
Hopefully, appreciation will lead to preservation of our rapidly disappearing landscape.

Wishing you well in your reading adventures.

Maria A Heugh

Outside my school bus window,
What do I see?
A world ever changing,
Is waiting for me.

To be on a school bus is
A really great treat.
It's the sights that you see,
When you sit in your seat.

The route may not vary
From day to day.
But you still never know
What you'll find on the way.

4

Abundant green leaves
That gave us summer shade,
Have started to alter.
They've started to fade.

6

Fall is the season.
It's a sight to behold.
Now, the trees are becoming
Red, orange and gold.

There's a cool, misty haze
That the sun filters through.
The spider's web sparkles,
Dressed in fresh morning dew.

8

We spy a blue Heron
In the marsh, by the creek.
See his long, slender neck,
And his sharp, pointy beak?

The school bus follows the route
On the way into town.
You can tell autumn's here,
If you just look around.

Up the street from the diner,
At the old hardware store,
A scarecrow and ghost
Wait outside the front door.

The school bus startles the blackbirds,
Who take to the sky.

They dip, dive and swirl,
In a cluster they fly.

The farmer is busy
In his field, making hay.
The days are much shorter;
There's less time to play.

The chill in the air is
No match for the sheep.
They nibble dry grass,
Wearing thick, woolen fleece.

Backhoes stretch, scoop and lift.
Bulldozers charge, shove and shift.
Trucks hauling pipes prepare to unload.
Change is coming to Elephant Road.

Leaves dance in the wind,
Past the angel of stone.
She sits on her wall,
Watching students leave home.

Outside my school bus window,
What do I see?
A world ever changing,
Is waiting for me.

The trees are all barren.
Their leaves blown away.
Where there once was bright color,
We see mostly gray.

Kids squeal with delight
At the snow covered hill.
What the driver needs now
Is patience and skill.

We turn left at the stop sign,
Then right at the light.
Past sidewalks and stores,
And their seasonal sights.

The cornfield is empty.
A few ears left behind.
What was dropped is soon eaten;
For the geese, it's a find.

The sturdy red barn,
With the paddock of stone,
Is the place for the winter,
The cows will call home.

"It will be over soon,"
Dad says with a quiver.
While he and his sons
Stand outside and shiver.

There's Chuck walking Opie,
On the road called Twin Brooks.
Sporting new winter coats,
Dressed for warmth and good looks.

Basements of cinderblock.
Frames made of wood.
Houses are built where
The bean field once stood.

The little stone angel
Watches snow as it lands.
Ever so gently,
In the palms of her hands.

Outside my school bus window,
What do I see?
A world ever changing,
Is waiting for me.

Just when we thought
We could take no more,
Spring arrives late in March,
With a wind, that's a roar.

Colorful bulbs
From the ground poke their heads.
They are yellow and white,
Purple and red.

29

The orchard explodes,
Like a great pink bouquet.
Honeybees have arrived.
They'll be busy all day.

Raindrops do more than
Help the grass grow.
With sunlight just right,
They bring out a rainbow.

We drive out of town.
"Look up, kids," I said.
A speckled, red hawk
Takes flight overhead.

A shy, ring-necked pheasant
Hides there, in the grass.
He'll come out to strut,
Only after we pass.

The woods are now green.
What a great bit of luck.
There's a doe with her fawn,
But no signs of a buck.

The cream colored foal
Tries to graze with her mare.
She's so tiny and cute,
You can't help but stare.

Black roofs and red shutters.
The sidewalks have been laid.
Soon, people will live
Where the fox always played.

Spring greets the angel
In a way that's so neat.
With soft, purple petals
That tickle her feet.

Outside my school bus window,
What do I see?
A world ever changing,
If you look, you'll agree.

Author Bio Page

Maria Hough became a school bus driver in 2001 after being a stay-at-home mother and aunt for many years. In addition to writing books, she continues to drive for the Pennridge School District in Bucks County, PA.

Mrs. Hough lives in East Rockhill, PA with her husband, children and various pets. Her writing inspirations come directly from her everyday life. She has several books in development and looks forward to sharing them with you soon.

All of the photographs are originals taken by Maria along her "School Bus Route" in Bucks County, PA.

Ordering Information

A signed copy of "Outside My School Bus Window" can be obtained by mailing your name, address and telephone number plus a check or money order for $10.47 ($7.97* plus $2.50 for shipping and handling) for each order to:

Wishing Well Press

1407 Schwenkmill Road
Perkasie, PA 18944
Telephone: (215) 258-1197
Email: wishingwellpress@netzero.net
www.wishingwellpress.com

You may also place an order via email by sending your name, address and telephone number to wishingwellpress@netzero.net.

*Please add 6% sales tax ($.48 per book) for orders mailed to a Pennsylvania address.
($7.97 + .48 + 2.50 = $10.95)

If you would like to schedule an author visit for your school, please use the above contact information.